TOOTH FAIRY
in Training

Michelle Robinson

illustrated by

Briony May Smith

My Tooth Fairy training starts today!
I'm learning from my sister, May.

May says, *"First thing fairies do is practise the old switcheroo.*

*Lift the pillow,
look beneath …*

leave the coins …

and take the teeth.

*Do it well and
you're a keeper.*

One rule, Tate:
don't wake the sleeper."

So I go gently.

Piece of cake!

May says,
"Now do it …

in a lake."

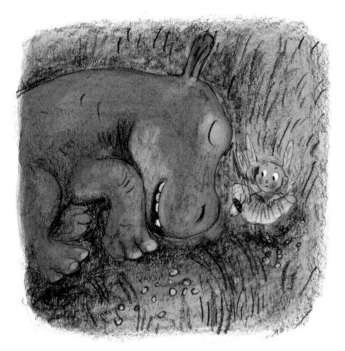

This baby hippo
needs a visit.

Not every child's a
human, is it?

"Careful," May says, *"some kids bite.*
Quick, Tate, we haven't got all night!"

I dry my wings
for visit two.

May says, *"Not the kangaroo.*

Your next tooth's waiting down that trail..."

I duck and dodge the mother's tail.

"Come on!" May says…

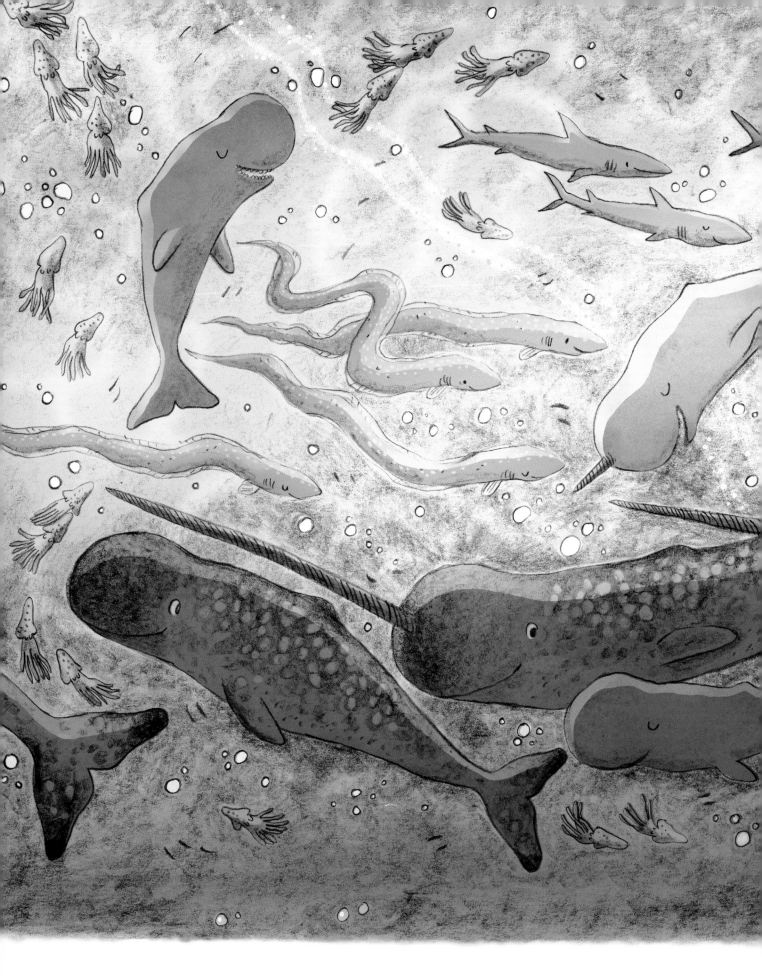

And down we go. She gurgles, *"Mind the undertow!"*

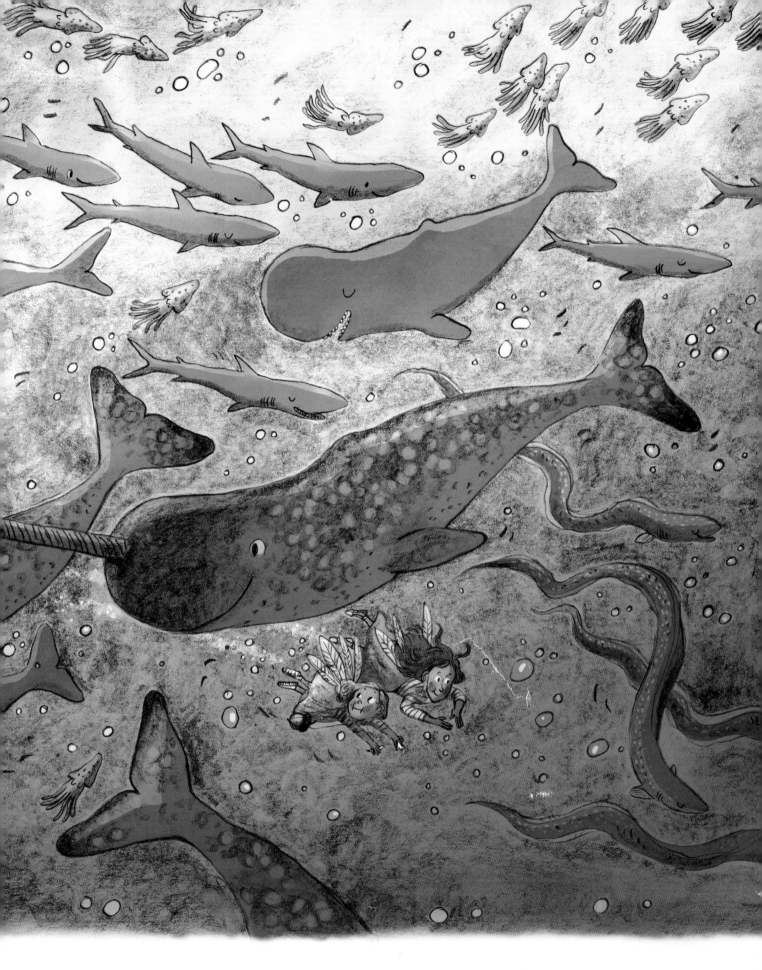

Squid, shark, narwhal, conger eel. *"Up next,"* May says...

"A fluffy seal."

I ask, *"This one?"* May says, *"The other."*

Oh dear — I think she means its brother.

It can't get worse than *that* now, can it?
We've almost done the entire *planet*.

Just a gentle
jungle wander ...

and a MASSIVE
anaconda.

Snakes lose teeth as well,
you know.

"And swallow fairies,"
May says. *"GO!*

Well done, Tate.
Snake teeth are rare.

One final tooth then
home, I swear."

A little girl.
I can't go wrong.

But hang on —
where's my money gone?

CLANG!

Oh no! She's woken! OW!

May says, *"We're in big trouble now!"*

Of all the teeth!
Of all the kids!
The sharks! The crocs!
The giant squids!

I had to get caught
by *Melissa* ...
doll-collecting,
fairy kisser.

I flap my wings. I make a wish.

I give my magic wand a SWISH!

Before Melissa knows what's hit her …
I've covered her in sleepy glitter.

Home at last, May's proud of me.
"You did it by yourself." Yippee!
Tooth Fairy Tate! I passed the test!
But even *fairies* need their rest.

It's lights-out time in Fairy Town.

May whispers as I snuggle down,
"We'll fetch more teeth tomorrow night—
Melissa lost one more. Sleep tight!"